www.postconcussioninc.com

POST CONCUSSION INC PUBLICATIONS

The information contained in this book is for informational and educational purposes only. The moral right of the author has been asserted.

PostConcussion_{Inc}

> **66**
>
> *Invisible injuries are tough to explain. The more we educate people the better it'll get.*

A Cookbook?

If someone told me that we would need another cookbook in the world I would have simply laughed but here we are! This cookbook is more than just a typical book you find in your bookstore. I wanted to create something for those who are struggling on the daily but still want to enjoy food as much as they can. The book progresses through phases to help you gauge what meals you're ready to make from easy to most difficult. There are symbols to help categorize some recipes for when you feel tired, dizzy and are struggling with memory. Recipes have extra steps to remind you when to take breaks and be successful in the kitchen.
I can't wait to see everyone's creations. Please be sure to tag us on social media so we can share!
I began to hate the task of cooking when ill and I hope this book helps you find that love again!

Love,

Bella

And thank you to chef Yota Chelf Dortlouke; this book would have never been created without your guidance and creativity!

About Bella

Bella is a brain injury advocate. After sustaining over ten concussions and experiencing post-concussion syndrome for nearly nine years, she realized that she could help others. Bella's multiple concussions completely rerouted her life from being a competitive athlete. Having to retire early and focus on her health was a long journey, involving both going to high school and college while ill. Bella's mental health deteriorated due to the drastic changes in her life and physical limitations.

After years of chronic headaches and much more, Bella began to improve. Three years ago, Bella hit a low spot and attempted to take her own life. After going to therapy, Bella knew she needed to do something for all those suffering from this invisible injury.

She started Post Concussion Inc because she believed something was missing in the world of brain injuries! Unlike most, she wants to aid not only individuals who have suffered from concussions but also their families and friends.

SYMBOLS
explained

Fatigue
For when you don't have a lot of energy, these recipes either don't involve many ingredients, steps or both!

Dizzy
These recipes offer breaks to sit down and don't require any loud equipment like a blender.

Memory
Limited steps to complete!

GLUTEN FREE   **DAIRY FREE**   **VEGETARIAN**   **VEGAN**

FATIGUE   **DIZZY**   **MEMORY**

The intended purpose of those symbols is to provide general information about each recipe. The vegan symbol refers to the vegan option given and the gluten-free symbol applies only if the ingredients used meet the gluten-free conditions. Please be mindful of the possibility of cross-contamination.

FRUIT COMBOS

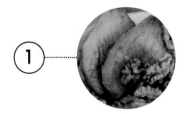

APPLES
& PEARS

Natural compounds found in apples
may help to stimulate the production
of new brain cells.

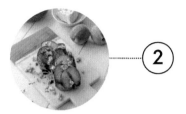

PEACHES
& COCONUT

Peaches have vitamin C and niacin
(vitamin B3) to help support brain
health and cognition.

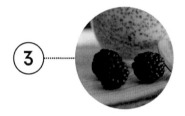

BLACKBERRIES &
MELON

Antioxidants in berry fruits help fight
free radicals and alter how brain
neurons communicate.

STRAWBERRIES &
PINEAPPLE

The antioxidants in strawberries
have a unique and important role in
brain health.

Tips
pairing

By combining acidic fruit, like citrus fruits, with sweeter ones, such as
peaches, pineapples and berries, you balance the taste palette of a recipe.

TABLE
OF
Contents

BREAKFAST

LUNCH

Breakfast

Strawberry Banana Smoothie

Ingredients

- 2 cups strawberries fresh or frozen, stems removed
- 1 banana fresh or frozen
- 1 cup milk, dairy or plant-based
- 1 scoop vanilla protein powder
- ½ tbsp honey, or agave/maple syrup, optional
- Ice, optional

Instructions

1. Add the strawberries, bananas, milk and protein powder to a blender or food processor. If you are using honey, agave or maple syrup and ice, add those to the mixture too and process for a few seconds until smooth and creamy.
2. Serve cold, optionally garnished with fruit.

Strawberry Banana Smoothie

serves: 2 | prep time: 5 mins | equipment: blender/food processor

Prep ahead:
Peel and chop the bananas into bite-sized pieces the night before and freeze overnight in a freezer-proof bag. Frozen bananas give a thick and creamy milkshake-like texture to the smoothie. Fresh bananas are just as good but the result will be less creamy. If you are using frozen bananas, you can skip the ice.

The antioxidants in strawberries fight off free radicals, which damage cells and can lead to memory loss and other brain difficulties.

Berry Ginger Smoothie Bowl with Nuts & Seeds

Berry Ginger Smoothie Bowl with Nuts & Seeds

   VEGAN GLUTEN FREE

serves: 2 | prep time: 5 mins | chilling time: overnight

The seeds and nuts in this delicious smoothie bowl contain significant amounts of zinc, which contributes to healing damaged tissue, growth of cells, building proteins, and supporting a healthy immune system.

Ingredients

- 4 cups frozen berries (preferably a mix)
- 2 cups orange juice
- 1 cup fresh spinach leaves
- ½ cup dates
- ¼ cup walnuts
- 2 tsp peanut butter
- 2 tsp flaxseed
- 1 tbsp sunflower seeds
- 1 tbsp pumpkin seeds

Instructions

1. Add the frozen berries, orange juice, spinach leaves and dates to a blender or food processor and process for a few seconds until smooth and creamy.
2. Pour the mixture into a bowl.
3. Top with walnuts, flaxseed, sunflower seeds and pumpkin seeds. Drizzle with peanut butter and serve immediately.

> Berries can prevent neurodegenerative diseases and improve movement and brain function.

 PostConcussion Inc

Yogurt Parfait with Fruit & Granola

Ingredients

- 1 ½ cup yogurt, dairy or plant-based
- 1 cup granola
- ½ cup fresh seasonal fruit, chopped
- 2 tbsp honey or maple/agave syrup
- 2 tbsp jam of choice

Instructions

1. Add a tablespoon of jam to the bottom of a jar or bowl.
2. Add a few tablespoons of yogurt and add a layer of fruit. Continue layering the yogurt and fruit until you run out of ingredients. Feel free to do this while sitting down.
3. Top with granola and fruit and drizzle with honey or maple/agave syrup. Serve cold.

Yogurt Parfait with Fruit & Granola

serves: 2 | prep time: 10 mins

This yogurt parfait with fruit and granola is the perfect way to start your day. There are very few combos that taste better than fruit and yogurt together, especially when they are combined with granola, jam, and honey or maple/agave syrup! Take a seat and make this delicious meal!

Granola is rich in monounsaturated and polyunsaturated fats, that increase cognitive activity.

Overnight Chia Pudding

Overnight Chia Pudding

serves: 2 | prep time: 5 mins | chilling time: overnight

A great idea for a balanced breakfast that can also be enjoyed as a healthy, high-protein snack.
Chia seeds contain quercetin, an antioxidant that fights free radicals in your body.
Energy levels are always changing, which is why making meals when we feel our best for later, can be a great solution.

Ingredients

- 4 tbsp chia seeds
- 4 tsp flaxseed, crushed
- 2 cups milk, dairy or plant based
- 2 tsp honey of maple/agave syrup
- 1 cup fresh, seasonal fruit to serve

Instructions

1. Combine the chia seeds with the milk, flaxseed and honey or agave/maple syrup into two jars or bowls and stir well.
2. Cover and refrigerate overnight or for a minimum of 2 hours.
3. Serve cold, topped with fresh fruit of choice.

> Chia seeds are rich in quercetin, an antioxidant, and fiber.

Chocolate Raspberry Oatmeal

Ingredients

- ⅔ cup oats, preferably steel cut
- 1 cup fresh raspberries
- 1 ½ cup milk, dairy or plant-based
- 2 scoops chocolate protein powder
- 2 tbsp shredded coconut

Instructions

1. Combine the oats, milk and protein powder in a medium sized saucepan over low to medium heat.
2. Cook for 3-5 minutes, stirring occasionally, until creamy.
3. Divide the oatmeal into your serving bowls, top with fresh raspberries and shredded coconut and serve hot.

Chocolate Raspberry Oatmeal

serves: 2 | prep time: 5 mins | cooking time: 5 mins

A filling and satisfying breakfast that you can have on the table in 10 minutes and enjoy year-round! Use fresh raspberries when they are in season, or frozen; just make sure to allow them to thaw for about 10 minutes prior to serving.

The flavonoids in berries have been shown to help improve coordination, memory and mood.

Eggs on Toast

Eggs on Toast

serves: 2 | prep time: 5 mins | cooking time: 10 mins

Eggs on Toast: A classic for a reason. Filling, easy to put together and packed with nutrients!
Coming up with ways to make eggs taste better with limited effort can be hard, which is why this recipe is perfect!

Leafy Greens are rich in brain-healthy nutrients like vitamin K, lutein, folate and beta carotene.

Ingredients

- 4 eggs, medium
- 4 slices whole-wheat bread, preferably country-style
- 2 cups mixed leafy greens
- 2 tbsp Greek yogurt
- 3 tbsp olive oil
- ½ tsp paprika
- 1 tbsp parsley, fresh, chopped
- Sea salt and freshly ground black pepper to taste

Instructions

1. Heat a dry pan over high heat and toast the bread for a few seconds on each side, until slightly golden.
2. Heat 2 tablespoons of the olive in the same pan and crack in the eggs. Turn the heat to medium-low and cook the eggs for 3-5 minutes with a lid on. Feel free to rest while the eggs are cooking, keeping an eye on them.
3. Spread the yogurt on the toasted bread, top with the eggs, season with salt, paprika and black pepper. Add a handful of leafy greens on the side, drizzle with olive oil and serve garnished with fresh parsley.

PostConcussion Inc

Easy Baked Eggs

Ingredients

- 4 eggs, medium
- 1 tbsp grated parmesan cheese
- 2 tsp olive oil
- 5-6 fresh basil leaves
- Sea salt and freshly ground black pepper to taste
- Optional: whole-wheat bread to serve

Eggs are rich in high-quality protein, omega-3 fatty acids, vitamins A, D, E, and B12, antioxidants and choline.

Easy Baked Eggs

serves: 2 | prep time: 5 mins | cooking time: 15 mins

Baked eggs make a fantastic breakfast or brunch and you can take this basic, simple formula and make it your own. Use up the herbs and spices you have in your pantry and experiment with different types of cheese, to serve a different version every time you make them.

Eggs were something I relied on heavily. I needed protein with the limited amount I was eating and I could always add different spices to change up the flavor!

Instructions

1. Preheat the oven to 180°C/ 356°F and brush two small baking dishes or ramekins with olive oil.
2. Crack two eggs into each ramekin and season with sea salt and freshly ground black pepper.
3. Bake in the preheated oven for 15 minutes, until the egg yolks are set. Set a timer and feel free to rest until the eggs are done.
4. Remove from the oven and sprinkle with parmesan cheese.
5. Garnish with fresh basil and serve hot.

Avocado Tomato Wraps with Olive Spread

Avocado Tomato Wraps with Olive Spread

serves: 2 | prep time: 5 mins | equipment: blender/food processor

A very easy and quick breakfast that doubles as a snack and is as healthy as it is delicious! You can toast the tortillas in a dry pan for 30 seconds on each side, over medium to high heat, to enhance the texture, before adding the ingredients, but they taste just as good as they are.

Ingredients

- 2 whole-wheat tortillas, optionally toasted
- 1 large, ripe avocado, pit removed
- 1 large tomato, stem removed
- ½ cup black pitted olives
- 6-8 leaves of fresh basil
- 1 tbsp olive oil
- Sea salt and freshly ground black pepper to taste.

Instructions

1. Thinly slice the tomatoes and the avocado. You don't need to be precise with the shape.
2. In a blender process the olives with the olive oil and fresh basil to get a thick paste. Add 1-2 tablespoons of water if the mixture is too thick.
3. Spread the olive mixture on the tortillas and add slices of avocado and tomatoes.
4. Roll and fold into a wrap. Serve at room temperature.

> Avocados are an excellent source of healthful unsaturated fat.

Pear & Walnut Oatmeal

Ingredients

- ⅔ cup oats, preferably steel cut
- ½ cup walnuts, roughly chopped
- 1 ½ cup milk, dairy or plant based
- 2 small pears
- 2 tbsp honey or agave/maple syrup
- 1 tsp ground cinnamon
- ¼ tsp ground nutmeg

Walnuts are rich in antioxidants and healthy fats. They may improve brain function and they add a lovely crunchy texture to any recipe!

Pear & Walnut Oatmeal

serves: 2 | prep time: 5 mins | cooking time: 15-20 mins

equipment: oven

Walnuts are rich in antioxidants and healthy fats. They may improve brain function and they add a lovely crunchy texture to any recipe! Pears are packed with nutrients that fight inflammation, especially when consumed with the peel. Just make sure to clean them thoroughly.

This recipe makes a wonderful winter breakfast and you can put your feet up and relax for a moment, while the pears are roasting in the oven.

Instructions

1. Preheat the oven to 180°C/356°F and line a baking pan with parchment paper.
2. Thinly slice the pears without peeling them. Remove any seeds.
3. Arrange the pear slices on the lined baking pan, drizzle with two tablespoons of honey/agave/maple syrup and sprinkle with a dash of cinnamon and nutmeg. Set a timer and roast in the preheated oven for 10 minutes until golden.
4. You can prepare the oatmeal while the pears are roasting, or take some time to rest and make the oatmeal when the pears are ready to come out of the oven.
5. To make the oatmeal, combine the oats, milk, a tablespoon of honey and a dash of cinnamon and nutmeg in a medium sized saucepan, over low to medium heat.
6. Cook for 5 minutes, stirring occasionally, until creamy.
7. Divide the oatmeal into your serving bowls, top with the roasted pear slices and walnuts and serve hot.

Smashed Chickpea & Feta Salad Breakfast Burritos

Smashed Chickpea & Feta Salad Breakfast Burritos

serves: 2 | prep time: 10 mins | cooking time: 5 mins

Breakfast burritos are a crowd-pleaser and this smashed chickpea and feta salad burritos will not disappoint! Choose whole-wheat tortillas and feel free to double the amount of mixed greens or raw leafy vegetables, to boost the fiber intake!

Ingredients

- 2 whole wheat tortillas
- 1 can (15oz/425g) chickpeas
- 1 small cucumber
- ¼ cup crumbled feta cheese
- 1 tsp paprika
- 1 tbsp olive oil
- Sea salt and freshly ground black pepper to taste.

> Whole wheat tortillas contain iron, B vitamins, manganese, and potassium.

Instructions

1. Drain and rinse the chickpeas in a colander, under cold tap water.
2. Place on a wide plate or bowl and mash with the back of a fork. Add the olive oil, paprika, salt and black pepper to taste and mix well to coat the chickpeas evenly.
3. Heat a non-stick pan and sauté the chickpeas for 2-4 minutes, until slightly golden and crispy. Remove from the heat.
4. Dice the cucumber into small dices and add to the chickpeas along with the crumbled feta cheese. Mix well.
5. Fill the tortillas with the mixture and fold into burritos. Serve immediately.

PostConcussion Inc

Lunch

Cherry Tomato Cucumber Salad

Ingredients

- 2 cups cherry tomatoes, halved
- 1 English cucumber, diced
- ½ red onion, thinly sliced
- ½ cup black olives, pitted, sliced
- ¼ cup feta cheese, crumbled
- 2 tbsp olive oil
- ½ lemon, juice only
- ½ tsp oregano
- Sea salt and freshly ground black pepper to taste

Instructions

1. In a large salad bowl combine the cherry tomatoes with the cucumber and onions. Mix well and add the olive oil and lemon juice.
2. Season with oregano, salt and pepper and mix well.
3. Top with black, pitted, sliced olives and crumbled feta cheese and serve at room temperature.

Cherry Tomato Cucumber Salad

serves: 2 | prep time: 10 mins

Fresh, delicious and ready in less than 10 minutes!

This cherry tomato-cucumber salad is the perfect summer light lunch, that doubles as a side dish.

Fisetin, an anti-inflammatory flavonol present in cucumber, is known to be important for brain health. Fisetin was found to prevent learning impairments and progressive memory loss.

Herbal Pesto Pasta

Herbal Pesto Pasta

serves: 4 | prep time: 5 mins | cooking time: 10 mins
equipment: blender/food processor

There's no reason to keep making the same pasta sauce recipes on repeat; once you've mastered the basic pesto routine, your midweek pasta lunch will become anything but boring!

Ingredients

- 4 cups whole wheat pasta of choice (you could also use quinoa, lentil or chickpea pasta)
- 1 cup extra virgin olive oil

- ¼ cup fresh basil leaves
- ¼ cup dill
- ⅓ cup cilantro
- 1 clove garlic
- 3-4 tbsp nutritional yeast
- 1 tbsp pine nuts
- 1 lemon, zest only
- Sea salt and freshly ground black pepper to taste

Nutritional yeast is a great source of vitamins and minerals. It also contains all nine essential amino acids, making it a complete protein, like those found in animal products.

Instructions

1. Bring a saucepan of salted water to a boil and cook the pasta according to packaging instructions.
2. Set a timer and feel free to rest while the pasta is cooking, or make the pesto to save time.
3. In a blender or food processor combine the olive oil, basil, dill, cilantro, garlic, pine nuts, lemon zest and nutritional yeast. Process to make the pesto, adding a bit of extra olive oil, if the consistency is too thick. Season to taste.
4. Mix the pesto with the pasta and serve hot, garnished with fresh herbs.

Yogurt Alfredo Pasta

Yogurt Alfredo Pasta

serves: 4 | prep time: 5 mins | cooking time: 10 mins

This is a healthier and lighter version of the classic Alfredo pasta, with Greek yogurt instead of heavy cream. The result intensifies the flavor profile of this simple pasta dish and brings out the aromas of the fresh herbs.

Ingredients

- 4 cups whole wheat pasta of choice
- 1 cup Greek yoghurt
- ¼ cup wine
- 3 cloves garlic
- 3-4 tbsp parmesan cheese, grated
- 3-4 tbsp seasonal fresh herbs, chopped (parsley, dill, basil)
- 2 tbsp olive oil
- Sea salt and freshly ground black pepper to taste

Regularly consuming probiotics through Greek yogurt, can lead to altered brain function, both while in a resting state and in response to an emotion-recognition task.

Instructions

1. Bring a saucepan of salted water to a boil and cook the pasta according to packaging instructions.
2. Set a timer and feel free to rest, while the pasta is cooking.
3. Heat the olive oil in a wide pan and sauté the garlic for a minute over medium heat, until soft and fragrant.
4. Add the wine and yogurt and stir to create a thick sauce.
5. Toss in the pasta and parmesan cheese and mix well to coat evenly.
6. Serve hot, topped with fresh seasonal herbs such as parsley, dill or basil.

Zucchini, Spinach & Parmesan Quesadilla

Zucchini, Spinach & Parmesan Quesadilla

serves: 4 | prep time: 10 mins | cooking time: 10 mins

Quesadillas re-invented!
Loaded with zucchini, spinach and parmesan, this is the most elegant and sophisticated version of a classic quesadilla. So tasty yet simple!

Quesadillas became an essential once I was able to stand for a few more minutes while cooking.

Ingredients

- 4 wholewheat tortillas
- 2 zucchinis, medium, grated
- 4 cups spinach leaves
- ¼ cup parmesan cheese, grated
- 2 tbsp fresh dill, chopped
- ½ lemon, juice and zest
- 2 tbsp extra virgin olive oil
- Sea salt and black pepper to taste

Instructions

1. Heat the olive oil in a wide pan and sauté the grated zucchini for 5 minutes, until all the liquids evaporate from the pan. Season with salt and pepper.
2. Add the spinach and stir to wilt down.
3. Remove from the heat and add the dill, lemon juice and zest. Mix well and fill the tortillas with the mixture. Add parmesan cheese and fold.
4. Optionally toast the folded tortillas in a dry pan until golden and serve hot.

> Spinach contains antioxidants, which fight oxidative stress and help reduce the damage it causes.

PostConcussion Inc

Roasted Carrot Soup with Turmeric & Ginger

Roasted Carrot Soup with Turmeric & Ginger

serves: 2 | prep time: 10 mins | cooking time: 45 mins
equipment: oven, blender/food processor

Sweet, flavorful, creamy and full of anti-inflammatory ingredients, this roasted carrot soup with turmeric and ginger, is definitely a cold-season winner.

Ingredients

- 5-6 carrots, large, halved
- 2 cups coconut milk
- 1 cup vegetable broth
- 1 yellow onion, small, diced
- 2 cloves garlic, minced

- 4 tbsp olive oil
- ⅔ tbsp fresh ginger, minced
- 1 tsp turmeric
- Sea salt and freshly ground black pepper to taste

Turmeric is a potent anti-inflammatory and antioxidant ingredient, that can boost brain-derived neurotrophic factor, due to the main active ingredient, curcumin.

Instructions

1. Preheat the oven to 200°C/400°F and line a baking pan with parchment paper.
2. Arrange the carrots on the baking pan and drizzle with 2 tablespoons of olive oil. Set the timer and roast in the oven for 15-20 minutes, until golden and tender. Feel free to rest while the carrots are roasting.
3. Heat the remaining 2 tablespoons of olive oil in a large saucepan over medium-high heat and sauté the onion and ginger for 5 minutes, until fragrant. Add the garlic and stir.
4. Add the turmeric and toast for 30 seconds, until fragrant.
5. Remove the carrots from the oven and add to the saucepan with the coconut milk and broth. Season with a pinch of salt and pepper. Cover and simmer over low heat for 15-20 minutes.
6. Using an immersion blender or food processor, blend the soup until creamy and smooth. Season to taste and serve hot.

Roast
Sweet Potato
& Feta Salad

Roast Sweet Potato & Feta Salad

serves: 2 | prep time: 10 mins | cooking time: 50 mins
equipment: oven

Let sweet potatoes, chickpeas and beetroots take the lead in today's lunch or tomorrow's dinner. This salad combines a naturally sweet flavor with hints of citrus, earthy notes and refreshing textures.

Ingredients

For the Salad
- 2 sweet potatoes, large
- 1 cup canned chickpeas, drained and rinsed
- 1 cup cooked beetroots, diced
- 2 cups mixed greens
- ½ red onion, thinly sliced
- ¼ cup feta cheese, crumbled
- 2 tbsp olive oil
- 1 tsp mild paprika
- Sea salt and freshly ground black pepper to taste

For the Dressing
- 4 tbsp extra virgin olive oil
- 4 tbsp orange juice
- 1 tsp honey
- 1 tsp Dijon mustard
- Sea salt and freshly ground black pepper to taste

Sweet potatoes are a great source of fiber, vitamins and minerals, and may enhance brain function by reducing inflammation and preventing free radical damage.

Instructions

1. Preheat the oven to 220°C/425°F and line a baking sheet with parchment paper.
2. Scrub the sweet potatoes and slice into ½ inch slices. Feel free to sit down while you are slicing the potatoes and preparing this salad.
3. Place the sweet potato slices in a bowl and drizzle with the olive oil. Season with paprika, salt and pepper and rub with your fingers to coat all the slices evenly.
4. Arrange the potato slices on the prepared baking tray, set the timer and roast for 20 minutes. Remove from the oven and add the chickpeas to the baking sheet. Mix to coat with the juices from the pan and return to the oven, set the timer for 5 more minutes and roast until golden and tender. Feel free to rest while the potatoes are roasting.
5. For the dressing, combine the olive oil with the orange juice, honey, Dijon mustard, a pinch of salt and black pepper. Whisk until creamy and thick.
6. In a large salad bowl, combine the potatoes, chickpea, beetroots, mixed greens and onions.
7. Top with crumbled feta cheese. Drizzle with the dressing and serve at room temperature.

Roast Peach & Blue Cheese Bruschetta

Roast Peach & Blue Cheese Bruschetta

serves: 2 | prep time: 10 mins | cooking time: 20 mins

equipment: oven

Sometimes all you need is a quick lunch that tastes amazing, without having to spend endless hours in the kitchen. Bruschettas are just that! Impress a friend when they come over for a quick visit, or make yourself something quick and delicious.

Ingredients

- 4 slices of country style bread
- 2 peaches
- ¼ cup blue cheese, crumbled
- 4 tbsp extra virgin olive oil
- 2 tsp balsamic vinegar, to serve
- Thyme, to garnish

> The plant-based polyphenols and prebiotics that are found in peaches, can decrease inflammation.

Instructions

1. Preheat the oven to 190°C/375°F and line a baking tray with parchment paper.
2. Cut peaches into ¼-inch-thick slices, and arrange on the prepared baking tray. Drizzle with 2 tablespoons of olive oil. Set the timer and grill the peaches for 5 minutes, until slightly golden and fragrant.
3. Brush the bread slices with the remaining olive oil and toast in the same pan for 2 minutes, until slightly crispy and golden.
4. Remove from the oven and arrange the peach slices on the bread.
5. Top with crumbled blue cheese, drizzle with balsamic vinegar, and garnish with fresh thyme/mint. Serve hot.

Quinoa Bake

Quinoa Bake

serves: 6 | prep time: 10 mins | cooking time: 30 mins
equipment: oven

This finger-licking quinoa bake will feed a crowd, without any extra effort. Which means, you let the oven work its magic, while you sit back and relax. Serve with some simple greens on the side and you have a nutritious and comforting meal. Make this large meal for many or make it for yourself, to reheat for multiple meals to come!

Ingredients

- 2 cups quinoa
- 5 cups button mushrooms, roughly sliced
- 2 cups cherry tomatoes, halved
- 2 leeks, large, thinly sliced
- 1 cup dried tomatoes, roughly chopped
- 1 red onion, diced
- 1 cup camembert cheese
- 4 tbsp extra virgin olive oil
- Sea salt and freshly ground black pepper to taste

Leeks may promote brain function due to the sulfur compounds that they contain. They may also protect your brain from age-related mental decline and disease.

PostConcussion Inc

Instructions

1. Bring a pot of salted water to a boil and cook the quinoa according to packaging instructions. Feel free to rest while the quinoa is cooking. Fluff the quinoa with a fork and set aside.
2. Preheat the oven to 190°C/375°F.
3. Heat the olive oil in a pan and sauté the mushrooms with the onions and leeks for 5-7 minutes, seasoning with salt and pepper.
4. In a baking pan mix the cooked quinoa with the mushrooms, onions, leeks, cherry tomatoes and dried tomatoes.
5. Add the fontina cheese on top. Set the timer and bake in the preheated oven for 10 minutes, until the cheese turns golden and bubbly. Feel free to rest in the meantime.
6. Serve hot.

Curried Lentil, Tomato & Coconut Stew

Curried Lentil, Tomato & Coconut Stew

serves: 2 | prep time: 5 mins | cooking time: 30 mins

A complete vegan lunch in a bowl! Rich and comforting, this curried lentil, tomato and coconut stew is packed with creamy, chewy, and hearty textures.

Ingredients

- 1 (14.5oz) can crushed tomatoes
- 2 cups vegetable broth
- 1 cup coconut milk
- 1 cup fresh baby spinach leaves
- ⅓ cup red lentils
- 1 red onion, chopped

- 1 clove garlic, minced
- 2 tbsp coconut or avocado oil
- 1 tsp curry powder
- ½ tsp chili flakes
- 1 bay leaf
- Sea salt and freshly ground black pepper to taste
- Optional: lime wedges to serve

Consuming curry powder may boost brain and digestive health. It stimulates the immune system and it has anti-inflammatory qualities.

Instructions

1. Heat the coconut or avocado oil in a large saucepan, over medium heat.
2. Sauté the onion for 5 minutes, until fragrant, and add the garlic, curry powder and chili flakes. Stir and cook for a minute before adding the lentils, tomatoes, bay leaf and spinach.
3. Add the broth and coconut milk to saucepan and simmer over medium to low heat, stirring occasionally, for about 20 minutes, until the lentils are tender. You could set a timer every 10 minutes and rest in between.
4. Season to taste with salt and pepper and serve hot with lime wedges.

Hummus Quinoa with Zucchini & Tahini Sauce

Hummus Quinoa with Zucchini & Tahini Sauce

serves: 4 | prep time: 10 mins | cooking time: 25 mins
equipment: blender/food processor

A hearty, make-ahead quinoa dish that will shine at family gatherings. Just because you're struggling doesn't mean you can't make a great family meal, take your time and use the broken-down steps to pace yourself.

Ingredients

For the Salad
- ½ cup quinoa
- 1 zucchini, large, stem removed and sliced into into ½" slices
- 1 cup cherry tomatoes, halved
- 1 cup fresh spinach leaves
- ½ cup canned chickpeas, drained, rinsed
- 4 tbsp extra virgin olive oil
- ½ tsp mild paprika
- Sea salt and freshly ground black pepper to taste

For the hummus
- 1 cup can chickpeas, drained, rinsed
- ½ cup tahini
- ½ clove garlic
- 1 lemon, juice
- 2-3 tbsp extra virgin olive oil
- Sea salt and freshly ground black pepper to taste

For the Tahini Sauce
- 4 tbsp tahini
- 2 tbsp lemon juice
- 1 tbsp extra virgin olive oil
- ½ tsp cumin
- Sea salt and freshly ground black pepper to taste

Quinoa is rich in antioxidants.

Instructions

Start with the quinoa:
1. Bring a saucepan of salted water to a boil and cook the quinoa according to packaging instructions. Feel free to rest while the quinoa is cooking.
2. Fluff with a fork and set aside.

Toast the chickpeas:
1. Heat 1 tablespoon of the olive oil in a wide pan.
2. Toast the chickpeas for a minute over high heat, seasoning with paprika, salt and pepper. Set aside.

Cook the zucchini:
1. Heat 3 tablespoons of olive oil in a pan and sauté the zucchini slices over medium-high heat for 2-3 minutes on each side, until golden but not too soft. Set aside.

Next make the hummus:
1. In a blender or food processor combine the chickpeas, tahini, lemon juice, garlic and olive oil.
2. Process until thick and creamy.
3. Season with salt and pepper. Set aside.

Next make the tahini sauce:
1. Whisk together the tahini, lemon juice, olive oil, cumin, salt and pepper.
2. Add a few tablespoons of water and mix again, if the consistency is too thick.

Assemble the quinoa bowls:
1. Arrange the quinoa, cherry tomatoes, toasted chickpeas, spinach leaves and zucchini in your serving bowls.
2. Top with a generous dollop of hummus. Drizzle with the tahini sauce and serve.

Snacks

Hemp, Almond & Blueberry Dip with Fresh Fruit & Pretzel

Hemp, Almond, and Blueberry Dip with Fresh Fruit & Pretzel

serves: 2 | prep time: 5 mins + overnight soaking

equipment: blender/food processor

If you are craving something sweet and fresh, this recipe hits all the spots. Set a timer before bed to soak the seeds and almonds overnight.

Ingredients

- 2 cups blueberries
- 1 cup Greek yogurt
- ⅔ cup hemp seeds, soaked in ½ cup water overnight, drained
- 1 cup almonds, soaked overnight in ½ cup water, drained
- 4 dates, pitted
- Zest of 1 lemon
- To serve: Fresh, seasonal fruit and a handful of mini pretzel

Instructions

1. Sieve the hemp seeds to remove the water.
2. In a blender combine the hemp seeds with the blueberries, almonds, dates, lemon zest and yogurt, to get a creamy dip.
3. Serve cold with fresh seasonal fruit and mini pretzel.

> Neuroimaging studies have shown that hemp modulates brain activity and connectivity in neural systems.

PostConcussion Inc

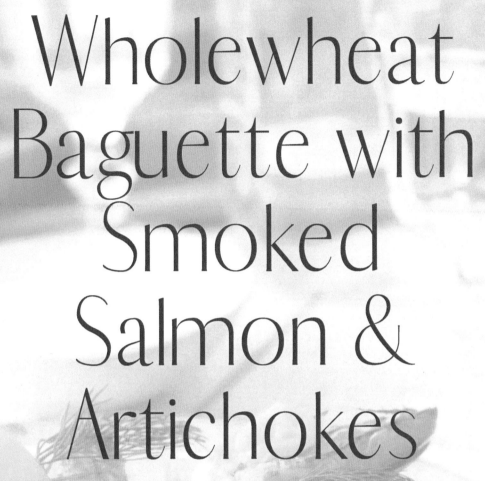

Wholewheat Baguette with Smoked Salmon & Artichokes

Wholewheat Baguette with Smoked Salmon & Artichokes

🚶 🧍

serves: 2 | prep time: 10 mins | cooking time: 5 mins

Smoked salmon and artichokes are a match made in culinary heaven. This simple baguette sandwich comes together in minutes and it tastes incredible!

Ingredients

- 1 whole wheat baguette
- 4 tbsp cream cheese, low fat
- 4 slices smoked salmon
- 3-4 artichokes from a can, cut in half
- 1 tbsp fresh dill
- ½ lemon, juice and zest
- 2 tbsp extra virgin olive oil
- Sea salt and freshly ground black pepper to taste

Instructions

1. Heat one tablespoon of olive oil in a pan and sauté the artichokes for 1-2 minutes until slightly charred. Set aside.
2. Cut the baguette in half and slice horizontally.
3. In a small mixing bowl, combine the cream cheese with the dill, lemon juice and zest. Season to taste with salt and pepper.
4. Spread the cream cheese mixture inside the baguettes. Add the salmon and artichokes.
5. Serve at room temperature, drizzled with olive oil.

> Salmon is full of Omega-3, a fatty acid known to be highly beneficial to the brain.

PostConcussion Inc

Oatmeal Chia-Tahini Protein Balls

Oatmeal Chia-Tahini Protein Balls

serves: 10-12 | prep time: 10 mins

These energy balls are packed with protein and they come together in 10 minutes or less! Store them in the fridge for a quick boost of energy. Perfect for when you need something to get you through the hard days.

Ingredients

- 1 ½ cups rolled oats
- ½ cup tahini
- ½ cup vanilla flavored protein powder
- ⅓ cup dark chocolate, grated
- 3 tbsp honey
- 2 tbsp almond milk
- 1 tbsp chia seeds
- 1 tsp vanilla extract
- A pinch of sea salt

Instructions

1. In a mixing bowl, combine all the ingredients into a dough.
2. Roll the mixture into balls with your hands and store in the fridge.

Protein powder contains several types of protein and amino acids that support brain function.

It's also rich in zinc, which can increase your physical and mental strength.

Dark Chocolate & Mint Protein Balls

Dark Chocolate & Mint Protein Balls

serves: 10-12 | prep time: 10 mins

equipment: blender/food processor

Layers of chocolate and mint that melt in your mouth, make these protein balls irresistible!

Ingredients

- 1 cup raw cashews
- ¼ cup unsweetened cacao powder
- 8 medjool dates pitted + soaked in water for 15 min
- 2 tbsp chocolate protein powder
- 1 tbsp chia seeds
- ¼ tsp peppermint extract
- 1 tsp almond milk
- Pinch of sea salt

Instructions

1. In a blender or food processor, combine all the ingredients and process to get a dough.
2. Roll the mixture into balls with your hands and store in the fridge.

> Cashews contain an adequate ratio between monounsaturated and polyunsaturated fatty acids. These two fats are crucial for maintaining brain health, assisting in memory and aiding in reducing inflammation.

Sweet
Mix Platter

Sweet Mix Platter

serves: 4-6 | prep time: 10 mins | cooking time: 5 mins

The beauty of this sweet mix plater lies in the simplicity of the ingredients.

Chose a high-quality dark chocolate and fresh seasonal fruit.

Ingredients

For the dark chocolate dip
- ½ cup dark chocolate chips or grated chocolate
- ¼ cup coconut cream

For the platter
- 1 ½ cup fresh seasonal fruit
- 1 cup dried fruit of choice such as cherries, figs, apricots, peaches, melon.
- ½ cup nuts of choice

Instructions

For the dark chocolate dip:
1. Heat the cream in a small sauce pan over low heat. Add the chocolate chips or grated chocolate and stir to melt.
2. Transfer in a small jar and place on the serving platter.

Assemble the mix platter:
1. Arrange the fresh fruit, dried fruit and nuts on the serving platter along with the dark chocolate dip and serve.

> Figs are a good source of potassium, a mineral that the brain needs to function properly. They also contain calcium, magnesium, iron, in addition to vitamin B-6, which can help the brain to produce neurotransmitters.

PostConcussion Inc

Savory
Mix Platter

Savory Mix Platter

serves: 4-6 | prep time: 10 mins | cooking time: 20 mins
equipment: oven

Mix platters are great for when having company over, but they are also great when you have a limited appetite; make this platter that you can routinely place in the fridge and take out again later when your appetite returns.

Ingredients

For the Potato Skins
- 2 russet potatoes, scrubbed
- 4 tbsp coconut cream
- 1 tbsp extra virgin olive oil
- Sea salt and freshly ground black pepper to taste

For the platter
- 1 cup radishes
- 1 cup carrot sticks
- 1 cup red pepper sticks
- ½ cup olives, pitted
- ½ cup cashew cheese
- A handful of rice crackers

For the apple chutney
- 2 cooking apples, peeled and diced
- 1 tbsp honey
- 2 tbsp raisins
- 1 red onion, finely chopped
- ½ tsp mustard seeds
- ½ tsp ground ginger
- 1 cup cider vinegar
- Sea salt and freshly ground black pepper to taste

Potatoes are rich in manganese, potassium and vitamin B6 and C, each known to assist in functions of the brain, while nerve centers respond positively to the fatty acids and amino acids.

Instructions

For the potato skins:

1. Line a large baking sheet with parchment paper and set a wire rack inside. Adjust oven rack to middle position and heat to 220°C/425°F.
2. Cut the potatoes into small wedges, scooping out a bit of the flesh, and place on the baking sheet. Season with salt and pepper. Drizzle with olive oil and bake in the oven for about 15 minutes, until crispy and golden.
3. Remove from the oven and set aside.

For the apple chutney:

1. Combine all the ingredients in a small saucepan. Bring the mixture to a boil, over medium heat and simmer uncovered, stirring frequently for 10-15 mins, or until thick and pulpy.
2. Remove from the heat and allow to cool.

Assemble the mix platter:

1. Arrange the potato skins on a serving platter and drizzle with coconut cream. Add the carrot and pepper sticks, chutney, cashew cheese, rice crackers, radishes and olives and serve.

Tortilla Pizza with Ricotta & Prosciutto

Tortilla Pizza with Ricotta & Prosciutto

serves: 4 | prep time: 10 mins | cooking time: 5 mins
equipment: oven

A light and easy snack, to keep your energy levels high!

Whole-wheat tortillas make an excellent base for a quick pizza and you can adjust the toppings to serve a different version each time.

Ingredients

- 4 whole wheat tortillas
- 1 cup ricotta cheese
- 1 cup kale, chopped
- 6-8 slices prosciutto
- 4 tsp extra virgin olive oil
- Sea salt and freshly ground black pepper to taste

Instructions

1. Preheat the oven to 180°C/350°F and line a baking pan with parchment paper.
2. Arrange the tortillas on the baking pan and spread the ricotta cheese on each one. Lightly season with salt and pepper. Scatter the kale on top and bake in the preheated oven for 5-7 minutes.
3. Remove from the oven, add the slices of prosciutto and serve hot, drizzled with olive oil.

> Kale provides several nutrients that may support brain health, like Omega-3 fatty acids, which can help improve your memory and brain performance.

Apple, Brie & Caramelized Onion Pita Pizza

Apple, Brie and Caramelized Onion Pita Pizza

serves: 2 | prep time: 10 mins | cooking time: 5 mins

equipment: oven

These apple, brie and caramelized onion pita pizzas are a delicious road to better brain health!
They are packed with flavor and so easy to pull off!

Natural compounds found in red apples, may help to stimulate the production of new brain cells.

Ingredients

- 2 whole-wheat pita breads
- 1 red apple, thinly sliced
- 4 oz brie
- 1 red onion, thinly sliced
- 1 tbsp honey
- 1 tbsp apple cider vinegar
- 2 tbsp olive oil
- Sea salt and freshly ground black pepper to taste
- Optional: Balsamic vinegar to garnish

Instructions

1. Heat one tablespoon of olive oil in a pan and sauté the onions for 1-2 minutes until fragrant. Season with a pinch of salt and pepper and add the honey and vinegar. Allow to caramelize over medium heat for 1-2 minutes.
2. Preheat the oven to 220°C/425°F.
3. Place the pita breads on a baking pan and spread a layer of brie on each one. Add apple slices and the caramelized onions and bake in the preheated oven for 5-7 minutes until golden.
4. Serve hot, drizzled with balsamic vinegar.

PostConcussion Inc

Beetroot Hummus with Spicy Tortilla Chips

Beetroot Hummus with Spicy Tortilla Chips

serves: 2 | prep time: 10 mins | cooking time: 5 mins

equipment: oven

An easy weeknight snack, perfect for lazy movie nights.

You can adjust the spiciness to your personal preference or use sweet or smoked paprika instead of cayenne pepper.

Ingredients

For the tortilla chips
- 2-3 wholewheat tortillas
- 2 tsp olive oil
- 1 tsp cayenne pepper
- Sea salt to taste

For the beetroot hummus
- 1 cup can chickpeas, drained and rinsed
- 1 beet, pre-cooked, chopped
- 2 tbsp tahini
- 2 tbsp lemon juice
- Sea salt and pepper to taste

> Spicy foods like cayenne pepper, increase circulation and cause your brain to release endorphins, helping to boost your mood. Tahini components have been shown to protect human brain and nerve cells from free radical damage.

Instructions

Preheat the oven to 180°C/350°F and line a baking pan with parchment paper.

<u>For the tortilla chips:</u>
1. <u>Lightly</u> oil the tortillas and season with cayenne pepper and salt. Cut in half and then cut each half in half again and then once again   to make the chips. Arrange the chips on the prepared baking tray and bake in the oven for 5 minutes, until golden and crispy.

<u>For the beetroot hummus:</u>
1. <u>In</u> a blender, process the chickpeas with the beet, tahini and lemon juice to get a creamy and thick hummus. Season with salt and pepper.

Serve the chips at room temperature with the dip.

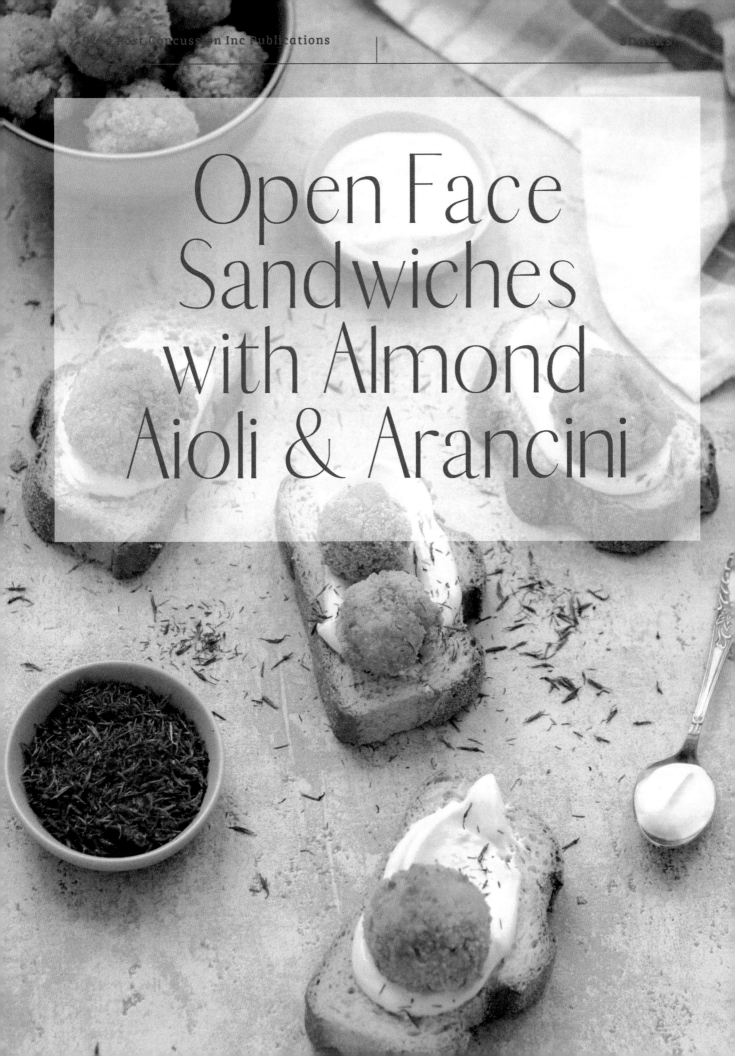

Open Face Sandwiches with Almond Aioli & Arancini

Open Face Sandwiches with Almond Aioli & Arancini

serves: 4 | prep time: 10 mins | cooking time: 25 mins
equipment: oven, blender/food processor

This is the best way to use up leftover rice and turn it into something exquisite, with minimal effort and maximum taste!

Ingredients

- 8 slices freshly baked country bread
- 1 tsp extra virgin olive oil

For the almond aioli
- ¾ cup vegan mayonnaise
- ⅔ cup blanched almonds
- 8-10 white seedless grapes
- ½ garlic clove
- 3 tbsp extra virgin olive oil
- 2 tbsp white vinegar
- 1 tbsp lemon juice
- Sea salt and freshly ground black pepper to taste

For the arancini
- 2 cups cooked rice, preferably arborio/risotto rice
- ⅔ cup wholewheat breadcrumbs
- 1 yellow pepper
- 1 green pepper
- 1 yellow onion
- 3-4 cloves garlic
- 3 tbsp extra virgin olive oil
- 1 tsp mild paprika
- 1 tsp tomato paste
- 1 tsp dried rosemary, chopped
- A pinch of saffron
- Sea salt and freshly ground black pepper to taste

Instructions

<u>Start with the arancini:</u>

1. Finely chop the onion, garlic and peppers. Heat a splash of olive oil in a pan and sauté for 3-5 minutes. Season with a pinch of salt, black pepper and dried rosemary.
2. Add the tomato paste and paprika and stir in the cooked rice. Mix well and remove from the heat. Add the saffron and stir.
3. Allow to cool while you are making the aioli. Feel free to sit down while you are working on that.

<u>Make the aioli:</u>

1. Combine all the ingredients except the mayonnaise in a blender and process until smooth. Fold in the mayonnaise and set aside.

<u>Continue with the arancini:</u>

1. Preheat the oven to 180°C/350°F and line a baking pan with parchment paper. Create small balls of the rice mixture with your hands, about 2 ½ inch/6 cm in diameter. Spread the breadcrumbs on a wide plate and roll the rice balls to coat evenly. Arrange on the prepared baking pan and bake for 10-15 minutes, until golden and crispy.
2. Brush the bread slices with a bit of olive oil and place in the oven for a minute, to slightly toast.

<u>Assemble and serve:</u>

1. Add dollops of the almond aioli on the bread slices, top with the baked arancini and serve hot.

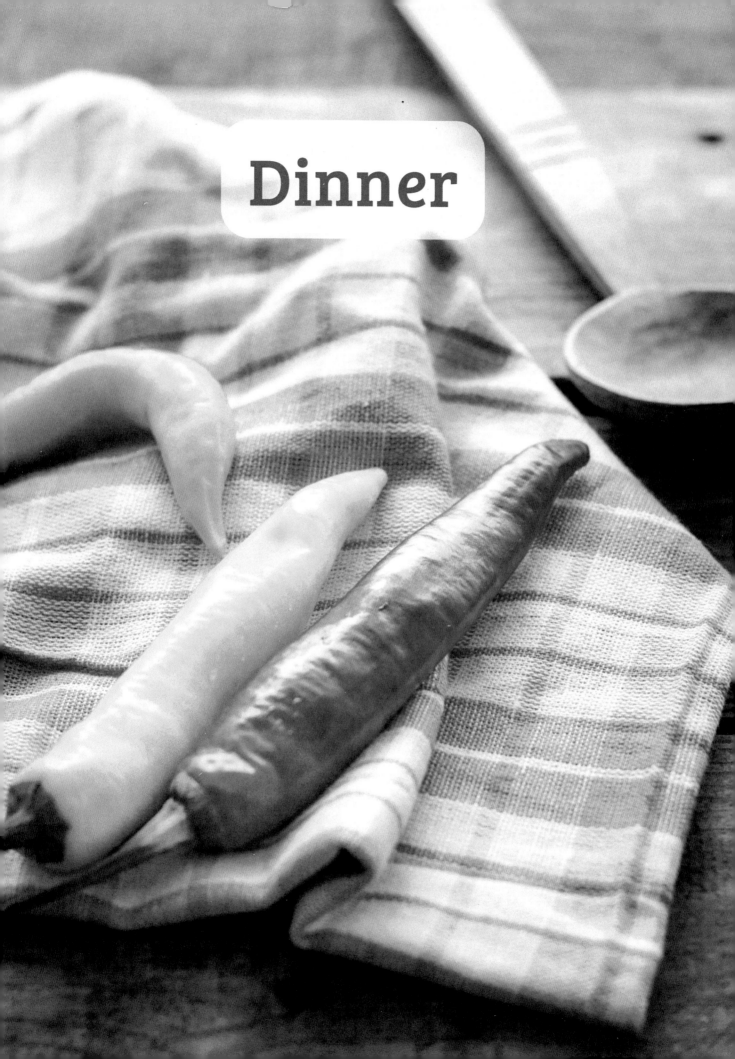

Dinner

Shrimp Stir Fry

Ingredients

- 4 cups shrimp, deveined and shelled
- 4 cups broccoli florets, fresh or frozen
- 2 bell peppers, any color, sliced into sticks
- 1 red onion, roughly chopped
- 2 spring onions, chopped
- 2 tbsp sesame oil
- Sea salt to taste

For the sauce
- ¼ cup low sodium teriyaki sauce
- 1 tbsp rice vinegar
- 1 tbsp minced ginger
- 2 tsp arrowroot powder
- ¼ tsp garlic powder

Arrowroot powder is packed with an impressive amount of thiamine, niacin, pyridoxine and minerals, including iron, magnesium, and as well as of antioxidants, vitamin E and omega fatty acids, that enhance brain power, cognition, and memory.

Shrimp Stir Fry

serves: 4 | prep time: 10 mins | cooking time: 20 mins

A delicious shrimp stir fry worth repeating every week!

Instructions

1. Whisk together the teriyaki sauce with the rice vinegar, arrowroot powder, ginger and garlic powder, to make a thick sauce.
2. Heat the sesame oil in a wide pan or wok and sauté the broccoli, onions, and peppers. Season with a pinch of salt and cook for 5 minutes. Add the shrimp and cook for 2 more minutes, until the shrimp are cooked through.
3. Pour the sauce into the pan and cook for a few minutes, until the sauce turns into a thick glaze. Serve hot, topped with spring onions.

Mediterranean Chickpea Skillet

Ingredients

- 2 cups can chickpeas, drained, rinsed
- 1 cup can crushed tomatoes
- 5-6 dried tomatoes
- 2 large bell peppers, any color, sliced
- 1 large sweet potato, diced
- 1 tsp oregano
- ½ tsp cayenne pepper
- Sea salt to taste
- Optional: fresh parsley to garnish

Dried tomatoes are packed with nutrients and anti-oxidants, including lycopene, that can neutralize free radicals and decrease inflammation.

Mediterranean Chickpea Skillet

serves: 4 | prep time: 10 mins | cooking time: 25 mins

A light, gluten and dairy-free, vegan dinner that will convert even the die-hard meat lovers!

Instructions

1. Heat the olive oil in a skillet and sauté the sweet potatoes with the peppers, dried tomatoes and chickpeas for 5-7 minutes, seasoning with salt and pepper.
2. Add the crushed tomatoes and cook for 10 more minutes, seasoning with oregano, salt and cayenne pepper, until the vegetables are tender and the crushed tomatoes turn into a thick sauce.
3. Serve hot garnished with fresh parsley leaves

Mushroom & Wild Rice Chowder

Ingredients

- 4 cups button mushrooms, sliced
- 4 cups vegetable broth
- 1 cup wild rice
- 1 ½ cup coconut milk
- 1 yellow onion, finely chopped
- 4 tbsp olive oil
- 1 tsp garlic powder
- Sea salt and freshly ground black pepper to taste
- Optional: gluten-free bread, toasted, to serve, herbs to garnish

Wild rice contains fibers and vitamins that improve blood flow throughout the brain and help memory function.

Mushroom & Wild Rice Chowder

serves: 4 | prep time: 10 mins | cooking time: 35 mins

A filling chowder to take you through the coldest winter nights.

Instructions

1. Heat the olive oil in a frying pan and sauté the mushrooms with the onions for 5-7 minutes, seasoning with garlic powder, salt and pepper.
2. Add the broth and coconut milk, bring to a boil over high heat and add the rice. Reduce the heat to medium-low and simmer, stirring occasionally for about 30 minutes, adding more broth if needed.
3. Feel free to rest in the meantime, setting a timer every 10 minutes to stir the chowder and check if you need to add more broth.
4. Serve hot with toasted, gluten-free bread and garnish with fresh or dried herbs.

Green Bean Casserole

Green Bean Casserole

serves: 4 | prep time: 10 mins | cooking time: 25 mins
equipment: oven

Green beans get a delicious makeover! Creamy and crunchy, this casserole is as healthy as delicious!

Ingredients

- 2 lbs green beans, fresh or frozen
- 4 cups button mushrooms, sliced
- 2 cups almond milk, room temperature
- 4 tbsp olive oil
- 4 tbsp buckwheat flour
- 1 tsp garlic powder
- Sea salt and freshly ground black pepper to taste
- Optional: crispy onions to serve

Beans are rich in Omega-3 fatty acids, which support healthy brain function and growth and regulate positive neurotransmitters in the brain, like serotonin and dopamine, that keep the mind healthy, alert and help maintain cognitive function. Buckwheat flour is high in tryptophan and magnesium, it promotes relaxation and is a great brain booster.

Instructions

1. Preheat the oven to 220°C/425°F.
2. Heat 2 tablespoons of olive oil in a frying pan and sauté the mushrooms for 3-5 minutes, seasoning with garlic powder, salt and pepper.
3. Add the beans and cook for 5 more minutes.
4. Transfer into a baking dish and set aside.
5. Heat the remaining olive oil and whisk in the buckwheat flour, to make a paste. Keep stirring until the paste turns slightly golden and then gradually pour in the milk in a stream, stirring constantly until it thickens. Season with salt and pepper.
6. Pour the mixture over the beans and bake in the preheated oven for 10 minutes, until golden. Serve hot, topped with crispy onions.

Roast Chicken & Vegetables

Roast Chicken & Vegetables

serves: 4 | prep time: 10 mins | cooking time: 30 mins
equipment: oven

A classic crowd-pleaser. You can't go wrong with roast chicken and vegetables, any day of the week.

Take your time to chop the vegetables while you are preheating the oven and feel free to use up any leftover vegetables you have in your fridge and pantry.

Ingredients

- 2 chicken breasts, cut in 4 pieces
- 4 bell peppers, any color
- 2 zucchinis
- 2 eggplants
- 2 potatoes
- 2 red onions
- 2 tbsp extra virgin olive oil
- 1 tsp dried thyme
- Sea salt and freshly ground black pepper to taste

Chicken is a great source of lean protein, offers a balance of brain-healthy compounds and is a good source of dietary choline and vitamins B6 and B12.
Onions have a natural flavonoid called fisetin, which helps improve long-term memory. Onions also contain quercetin and anthocynanin, which have been shown to improve concentration.

Instructions

1. Preheat the oven to 220°C/425°F.
2. Gather all the vegetables and feel free to sit comfortably in front of your kitchen counter or table with your chopping board.
3. Chop the bell peppers, zucchinis, eggplants, potatoes and red onions into bite-sized pieces.
4. Place on a baking pan and add the chicken breasts. Lightly coat with olive oil and season with salt and pepper.
5. Bake in the preheated oven for about 30 minutes, until the vegetables are tender and the chicken completely cooked through.
6. Remove from the oven and season with thyme. Serve hot.

Eggplant Traybake with Zaatar & Olive Oil

Eggplant Traybake with Zaatar & Olive Oil

serves: 4 | prep time: 10 mins | cooking time: 35 mins
equipment: oven

Eggplants, zaatar and olive oil are a match made in heaven.

This is a very simple meal, that bursts with flavors and good nutrients!

Ingredients

- 4 large eggplants
- 1 ½ cup can chickpeas
- 1 red onion
- 1 lemon, cut in wedges
- 5 tbsp extra virgin olive oil
- 2-3 tsp zaatar
- 1 tsp garlic powder
- Sea salt and freshly ground black pepper to taste

Packed with antioxidants and nutrients that boost the immune system, zaatar fights inflammation and increases circulation that aids memory.

Instructions

1. Preheat the oven to 220°C/425°F.
2. Cut each eggplant into 4 long wedges. Arrange the wedges on a large baking pan.
3. Drain and rinse the chickpeas and toss on the eggplants.
4. Slice and add the onions.
5. In a small bowl, mix the olive oil with the zaatar and garlic powder, a pinch of sea salt and black pepper.
6. Drizzle the mixture over the eggplants and chickpeas, set the timer and bake in the preheated oven for 30-35 minutes, until the eggplants are completely cooked through and the chickpeas are golden. Feel free to rest in the meantime. Serve hot with lemon wedges.

Gnocchi Casserole in Tomato Sauce

Ingredients

- 4 cups gluten-free and dairy-free gnocchi
- 2 cups tomato sauce
- 1 red onion, finely chopped
- 1 carrot, diced
- 2 cloves garlic, minced
- ½ cup celery, finely chopped
- 2 tbsp extra virgin olive oil
- 2 bay leaves
- Sea salt and freshly ground black pepper to taste

Celery is a rich source of luteolin, a plant compound believed to reduce inflammation in the brain.

Gnocchi Casserole in Tomato Sauce

serves: 2 | prep time: 10 mins | cooking time: 25 mins

equipment: oven

A hearty casserole for the entire family.

Instructions

1. Preheat the oven to 220°C/425°F.
2. Heat the olive oil in a frying pan and sauté the onions with the carrots and celery for 3-5 minutes, until tender and fragrant. Season with a pinch of salt and pepper and add the minced garlic. Mix well and add the tomato sauce and bay leaves. Season with salt and pepper and simmer for 5 minutes.
3. Add the gnocchi to a baking pan and cover with the tomato sauce.
4. Set a timer and bake in the preheated oven for 15 minutes, until the gnocchi are cooked through, adding a bit of water if needed and stirring to cook all the gnocchi evenly. Serve hot.

Dahi Dal

Ingredients

- 1 cup split moong dal (yellow lentils or lentils of your choice)
- 4 cups fresh spinach leaves
- 2 tbsp vegetable oil or ghee
- 2 yellow onions, finely chopped
- ½ tsp ground turmeric
- 1 tbsp ginger, roughly chopped
- 1 tsp chili powder
- 3 tbsp coconut yogurt
- Sea salt to taste

Loaded with B vitamin folate, lentils have a reputation for strengthening brain power. Folate also decreases amino acid levels, which often contribute to impaired functioning of the mind.

Dahi Dal

serves: 4 | prep time: 10 mins | cooking time: 25 mins

equipment: blender/food processor

Indian food at its finest.

Instructions

1. Place the moong dal in a sauce pan and cover with water. Add a pinch of salt, turmeric and ginger and bring to a boil for 10 minutes. Set the timer while you rest and return to add the spinach. Cook for another 5 minutes.
2. Next, heat the vegetable oil or ghee in a frying pan and sauté the onions over low to medium heat for 10 minutes, seasoning with the chili powder.
3. Return to the lentils and using a stick blender, process them to make a puree.
4. Return to the pan, add the coconut yogurt and mix. Serve hot.

Slow Cooked Ground Turkey & Cocoa Chili

Slow Cooked Ground Turkey & Cocoa Chili

serves: 4 | prep time: 10 mins | cooking time: 60 mins

Put your feet up and relax, while this aromatic, slow-cooked chili is simmering over low heat.

Ingredients

- 1 red onion chopped
- 2 chili peppers seeded and chopped
- 2 tsp chili powder
- 1 tsp ground cumin
- 1 tsp ground coriander
- 2 cups ground turkey
- 2 cloves garlic, minced
- 1 tbsp tomato paste
- 1 tbsp unsweetened cocoa powder
- 1 large sweet potato peeled and diced into 1-inch cubes
- 1 cup can kidney beans, drained and rinsed
- ½ cup can crushed tomatoes
- 2 cups chicken broth
- 3 tbsp olive oil
- Sea salt and freshly ground black pepper to taste
- Optional: fresh cilantro to serve

Chili peppers contain a compound known as apigenin, which has been shown to strengthen connections between brain cells.

Instructions

1. Heat the olive oil in a large heavy-bottomed saucepan over medium to high heat.
2. Sauté the onion with the chili peppers, seasoning with chili powder, ground cumin and ground coriander for 5-7 minutes.
3. Add in the ground turkey and cook, mixing well for 5 minutes.
4. Stir in the garlic and tomato paste and cook for a few more seconds.
5. Add in the cocoa powder, sweet potatoes, kidney beans, tomatoes, chicken stock and season lightly with salt and black pepper.
6. Bring it to a boil and then reduce the heat to medium-low, letting it simmer for 40-45 minutes. Set a timer and feel free to rest.
7. Serve hot, garnished with fresh cilantro leaves.

Watermelon Tomato Salad with Vegan Cheese & Homemade Gluten-Free Croutons

Watermelon Tomato Salad with Vegan Cheese & Homemade Gluten-Free Croutons

serves: 4 | prep time: 10 mins | cooking time: 5 mins

equipment: blender/food processor

This recipe pairs together watermelon and tomatoes, two of summer's favorites, and teaches you how to make your own vegan cheese at home, in just a few minutes!

Ingredients

For the vegan cheese
- 1½ cups blanched almonds
- 1 garlic clove
- 1 tbsp nutritional yeast
- 2 tbsp lemon juice
- Filtered water as needed
- Sea salt to taste

For the croutons
- 2-3 slices gluten-free bread, diced
- 1 tsp olive oil
- Pinch of sea salt to taste

For the salad
- 4 cups medium cubed watermelon, seeds removed
- 4 cups chopped heirloom tomatoes
- 2 tbsp olive oil
- 2 tbsp lemon juice
- 1 tsp Dijon mustard
- ¼ tsp sea salt and freshly ground black pepper to taste
- Fresh basil or mint to serve

> Watermelon has high concentrations of antioxidants, including lycopene, which may help prevent cognitive decline. It also offers a strong complement of beta-carotene.

Instructions

Start with the cheese:

1. In a food processor combine the blanched almonds with the garlic, nutritional yeast and lemon juice. Add a pinch of salt and process adding water in a stream (about ½ cup), until you get a creamy ricotta-like consistency. Set aside.

Next make the croutons:

1. Heat the olive oil in a non-stick pan and toast the gluten-free bread cubes for 2-3 minutes, until golden. Season with salt and set aside.

Make the dressing:

1. Whisk together the olive oil with the lemon juice and mustard. Set aside.

Assemble the salad:

1. Place the watermelon and the tomatoes in a salad bowl, drizzle with the dressing and add dollops of the cheese. Top with the croutons and garnish with fresh basil or mint leaves.

Serve at room temperature.

Disclaimer

The information contained in or made available through Post Concussion Inc cannot replace or substitute for the services of trained professionals in any field, including, but not limited to, financial, medical, psychological, or legal matters. In particular, you should regularly consult a doctor in all matters relating to physical or mental health, particularly concerning any symptoms that may require diagnosis or medical attention. We and our licensors or suppliers make no representations or warranties concerning any treatment, action, or application of medication or preparation by any person following the information offered or provided within or through Post Concussion Inc. Neither we nor our partners, or any of their affiliates, will be liable for any direct, indirect, consequential, special, exemplary or other damages that may result, including but not limited to economic loss, injury, illness or death.

You alone are responsible and accountable for your decisions, actions and results in life, and by your use of the Post Concussion Cookbook, you agree not to attempt to hold us liable for any such decisions, actions or results, at any time, under any circumstance.

This disclaimer governs your use of the Post Concussion Cookbook.
By using this book, you accept this disclaimer in full.
If you disagree with any part of this disclaimer, do not use this book or any affiliated websites, properties, or companies.

Where to find us

PODCAST: POSTCONCUSSIONINC.COM

Concussions are invisible and so is post-concussion syndrome.
The Post Concussion Podcast digs down into the realities of living with concussions and what it's like when things don't go back to normal. Get the truth about what it's like to be around someone with a concussion and what it's like to have one. Not just for individuals with concussions but for parents, friends, siblings, coaches, and everyone else who wants to understand more

SUPPORT NETWORK: CONCUSSIONCONNECT.COM

A place for everyone related to the concussion/brain injury community!
We understand the need for a safe place to go separate from your regular social world, less overwhelming and more personal. Join Concussion Connect to have a place to share and get support along your survivor journey!
Though a place for survivors, we also welcome all loved ones and professionals who are out to learn more about this invisible injury.